Conquer Year 5 Science with CGP!

Ready to test the key facts in Year 5 Science? Once pupils have got to grips with all the content in our matching Year 5 Science Knowledge Organiser, they can check how much they've learned with our Knowledge Retriever!

With bonus mixed practice quizzes and a full set of answers too, this book has everything Year 5 pupils need for Science success!

CGP – still the best! ☺

Our sole aim here at CGP is to produce the highest quality books — carefully written, immaculately presented and dangerously close to being funny.

Then we work our socks off to get them out to you — at the cheapest possible prices.

Contents

Published by CGP.

Editors: Josie Gilbert, Jake McGuffie, Luke Molloy, Charlotte Sheridan and George Wright
Contributor: Paddy Gannon

With thanks to Kate Whitelock for the proofreading.
With thanks to Jan Greenway for the copyright research.

ISBN: 978 1 78908 957 8

Printed by Elanders Ltd, Newcastle upon Tyne.
Clipart from Corel®
Illustrations by: Sandy Gardner Artist, email sandy@sandygardner.co.uk

Based on the classic CGP style created by Richard Parsons.

How to Use This Book

This book is split into different topics that you'll learn about in Year 5 Science. Every page in this book has a matching page in the Year 5 Science **Knowledge Organiser**. Before you fill in the pages in this book, you should have learnt about the topic in your lessons at school and in the Knowledge Organiser.
This is what you need to do:

1 Read the pages and fill in any dotted lines as you go. One dotted line means there's one word missing — sometimes you get given the first letter of the word and sometimes you don't.

2 When you've finished, you can use the answers at the back of the book to check your work. Tick the smiley face to show how well you know the topic.

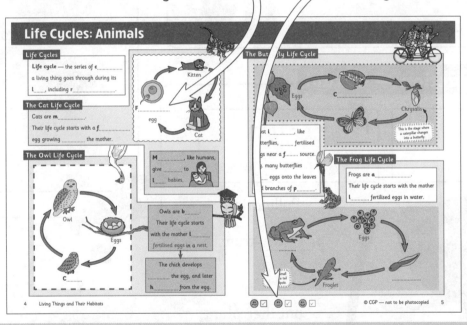

Sometimes you might have used a different word to fill in the gap from what is shown in the answers. That's okay, as long as the word has the same meaning.

There are also **Quizzes** throughout the book:

- These quizzes test content from the previous few pages, including key words. There's also a bigger 'Mixed Quiz' at the end that tests content from the whole book.

- Answers to the quizzes are at the back of the book.
  After you've completed a quiz, mark your answers and write your score in the box at the end of the quiz.

Reproduction

Reproduction

Reproduction: When new **l**............ things

are made, e.g. baby animals or new plants.

Two types of reproduction:

1 **A**....................

Only .... parent needed.

2 **S**................

Two parents needed —

a male and a ....

Animal Reproduction

Animals reproduce

by .... reproducti...

.... from female

.... from male

Plant Reproduction — Sexual

Stigma: .... part of flower.

P..............: From **m**........ part of flower.

Pollination —

P............ transferred to the **s**.............. of another plant.

.... fertilised by the **p**............

Fertilised .... becomes a ....

S.......... germinate into a **s**...................

Fertilised .... becomes a ....

Sperm **f**.................... egg.

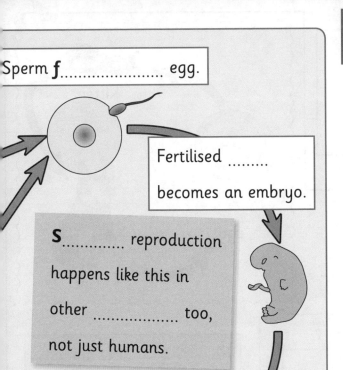

Fertilised .... becomes an embryo.

S............ reproduction happens like this in other .... too, not just humans.

Embryo grows into a **b**...........

S.............. grows into a plant.

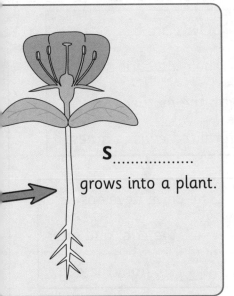

Plant Reproduction — Asexual

In asexual reproduction, **n**......... plants grow from parts of a parent plant (without using **p**............ and **e**.........).

Gardeners can use this method, e.g.:

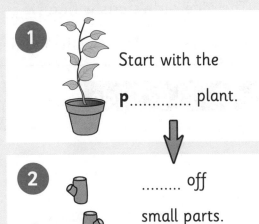

1 Start with the **p**.............. plant.

2 .... off small parts.

3 Put the small parts in **s**.........

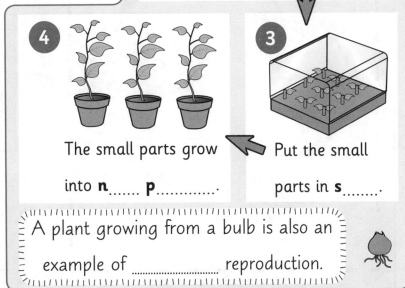

4 The small parts grow into **n**........ **p**..............

A plant growing from a bulb is also an example of .... reproduction.

Life Cycles: Animals

Life Cycles

Life cycle — the series of **c**................. a living thing goes through during its **l**........, including **r**.............................

The Cat Life Cycle

Cats are **m**....................

Their life cycle starts with a **f**....................... egg growing .... the mother.

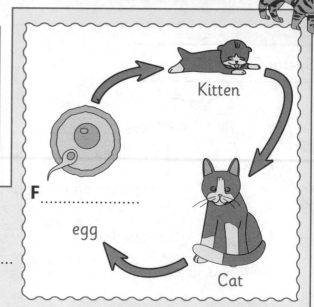

Kitten

F.....................

egg

Cat

M..................., like humans, give .... to **l**........ babies.

The Owl Life Cycle

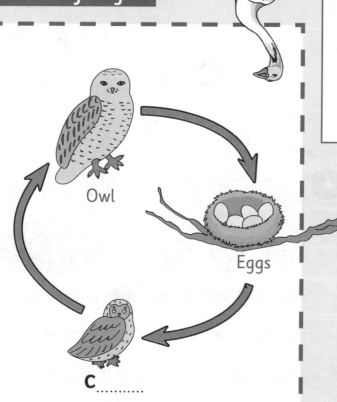

Owl

Eggs

C............

Owls are **b**...........

Their life cycle starts with the mother **l**............. fertilised eggs in a nest.

The chick develops .... the egg, and later **h**................. from the egg.

The Butterfly Life Cycle

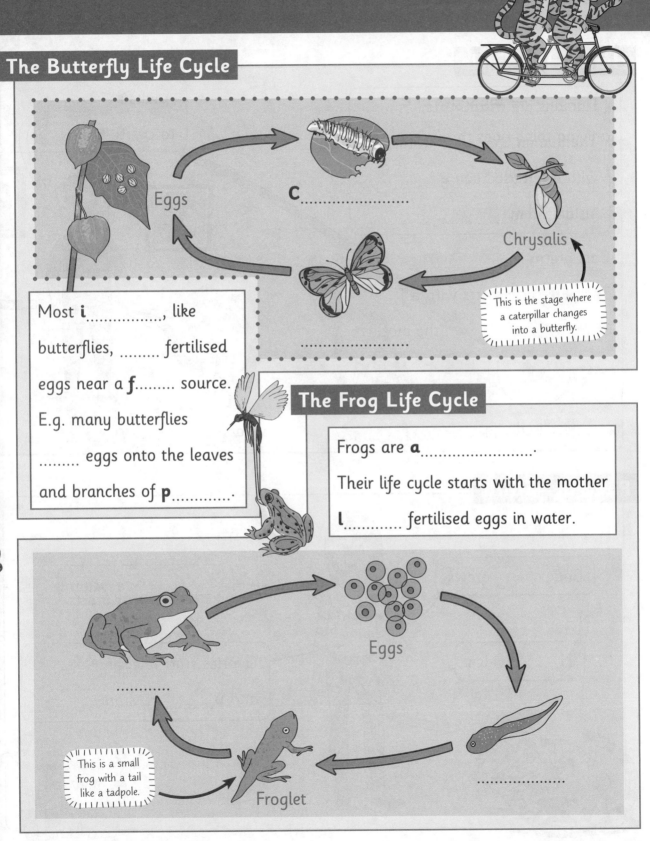

Eggs

c.....................

Chrysalis

This is the stage where a caterpillar changes into a butterfly.

....

Most **i**.............., like butterflies, ... fertilised eggs near a **f**......... source. E.g. many butterflies .... eggs onto the leaves and branches of **p**..............

The Frog Life Cycle

Frogs are **a**.........................

Their life cycle starts with the mother **l**............. fertilised eggs in water.

Eggs

This is a small frog with a tail like a tadpole.

Froglet

....

....

Life Cycles: Humans

Human Life Cycle

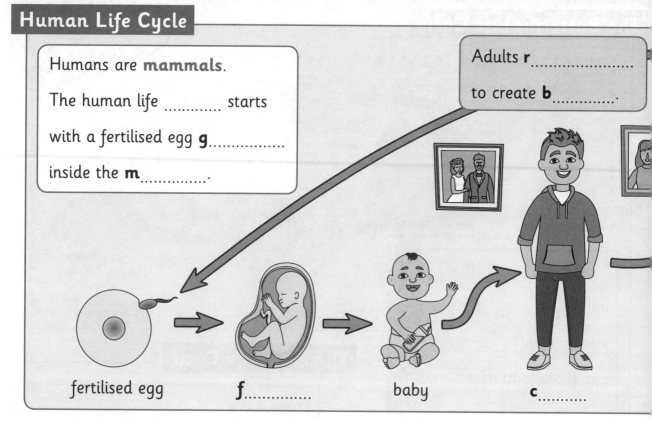

Humans are **mammals**.

The human life .... starts with a fertilised egg **g**................ inside the **m**................

Adults **r**........................ to create **b**.............

fertilised egg

f................

baby

c............

Puberty — Girls

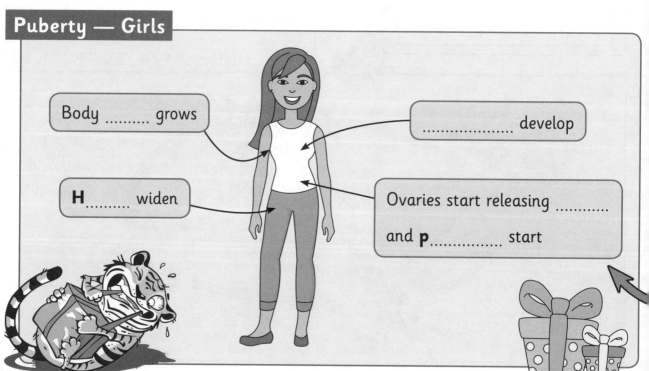

Body .... grows

H............ widen

.... develop

Ovaries start releasing .... and **p**................ start

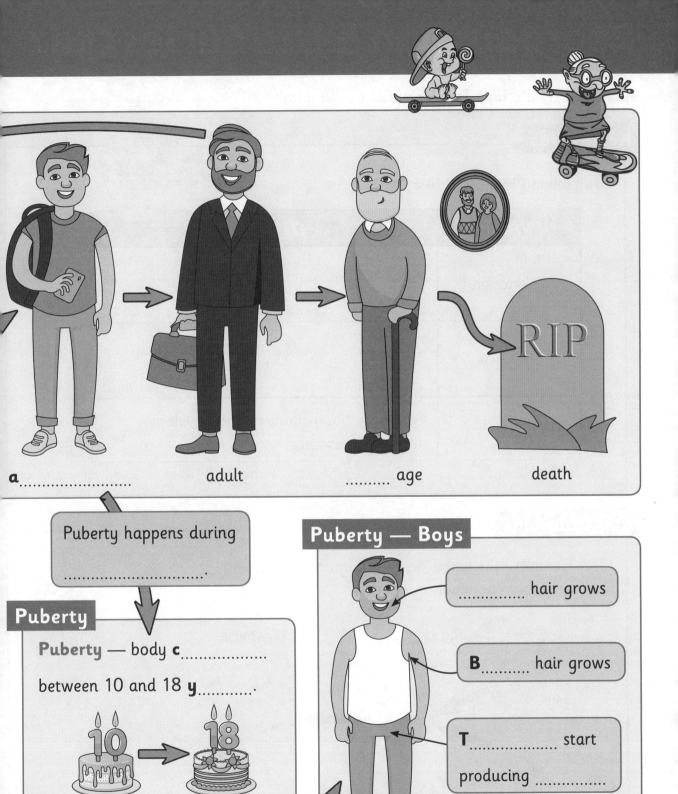

a..........................   adult   .... age   death

Puberty happens during

....

Puberty

Puberty — body **c**...................

between 10 and 18 **y**............ .

Different for .... and **b**........ .

Puberty — Boys

.... hair grows

B............ hair grows

T.................... start

producing ....

Reproduction & Life Cycles Quiz

Buckle up — it's time for the quiz of a life cycle!

Key Words

1. Fill in the gaps in this table.

Word	Definition
Pollination	....
Life cycle	....
....	When the body changes and develops during adolescence.

_____
3 marks

Key Diagrams

2. Complete the labels on this diagram showing sexual reproduction in animals.

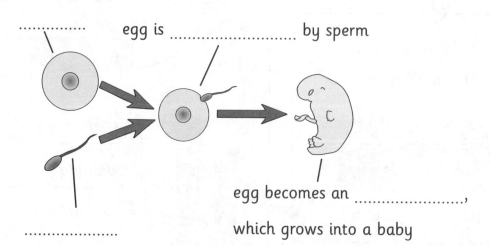

....   egg is .... by sperm

egg becomes an ....,

which grows into a baby

....

_____
4 marks

3. Write down which animal best fits each description
   — cat, butterfly, owl or frog.

   a) This animal gives birth to live babies.

   ....

   b) This animal hatches from an egg in a nest.

   ....

   2 marks

4. Give three examples of how girls' bodies change during puberty.

   1. ....

   2. ....

   3. ....

   3 marks

5. Write down whether each of these statements is true or false.

   After adolescence, humans reach adulthood.   ....

   A chrysalis is a stage in a frog's life cycle.   ....

   Some plants can reproduce asexually.   ....

   3 marks

6. Complete the gaps to describe sexual reproduction in plants.

   .... from one flower is transferred to the

   .... of another flower. This causes an egg

   to be .... and become a seed. The seed

   .... into a seedling, which will become a plant.

   4 marks

Score:

9

Comparing Everyday Materials

Hardness

.... materials are difficult

to scratch or bend. E.g.

steel hammer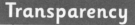

diamond-edged saw

Materials that aren't

hard are .... E.g.

cushions and

mattresses

Transparency

.... materials

are see-through, e.g. glass.

O.............. materials

are not see-through,

e.g. thick curtain fabric.

Different materials have different

p..................., e.g. hard, soluble,

magnetic, etc. The **p**.................. of

a material affect what we use it for.

Magnetic Materials

Some metals can be **m**..................... (**a**...................... to magnets),

while non-metals can't.

But not all metals are ...., e.g.

Aluminium

Steel

Iron and steel are magnetic
but aluminium, brass and
copper are not.

Conductors of Electricity

Electricity can flow through

electrical **c**.......................

E.g. **m**.......... pins

and copper **w**.........

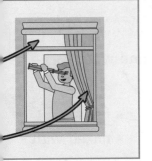

Solubility

I................... materials don't dissolve,
e.g. metal spoon and **c**............... mug.

S............... materials dissolve,
e.g. sugar cubes.

Conductors of Heat

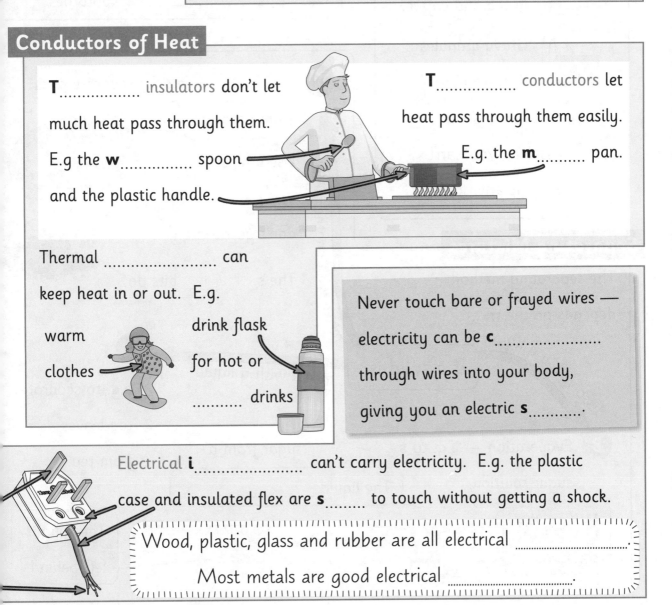

T................. insulators **don't let**
much heat pass through them.
E.g the **w**............... spoon
and the plastic handle.

T................... conductors **let**
heat pass through them easily.
E.g. the **m**.......... pan.

Thermal .... can
keep heat in or out. E.g.

warm
clothes

drink flask
for hot or
.... drinks

Never touch bare or frayed wires —
electricity can be **c**.........................
through wires into your body,
giving you an electric **s**............

Electrical **i**..................... can't carry electricity. E.g. the plastic
case and insulated flex are **s**......... to touch without getting a shock.

Wood, plastic, glass and rubber are all electrical ....

Most metals are good electrical ....

Separating & Changing Materials

Dissolving

Some solids .... in liquids to form a **s**................. .

For example:

S........... dissolves in tea and coffee.

Gravy granules dissolve in **w**........... .

When a solid dissolves, you can't s........ it anymore.

Mixtures

Rice in water

A **s**............... of salt and water

A mixture is just things mixed **t**................. .

Peas mixed with potatoes

Separating Mixtures

The separating method depends on the **m**................. :

If a solid is:

mixed with another solid

mixed with a liquid

dissolved in a liquid

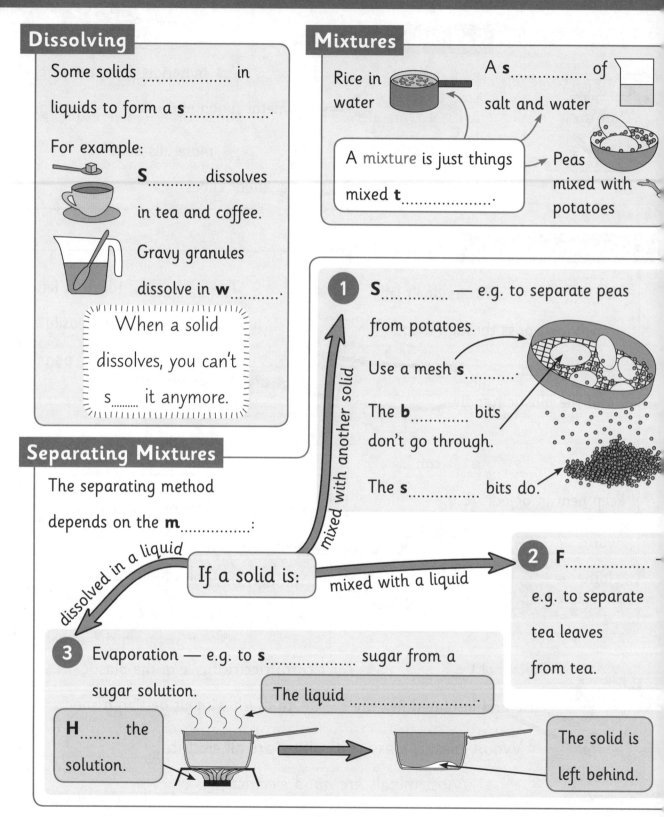

1. **S**............... — e.g. to separate peas from potatoes.

   Use a mesh **s**........... .

   The **b**........... bits don't go through.

   The **s**............... bits do.

2. **F**................. e.g. to separate tea leaves from tea.

3. Evaporation — e.g. to **s**................. sugar from a sugar solution.

   The liquid ....

   H......... the solution.

   The solid is left behind.

Reversible Changes

After a reversible change, the material **l**............. and **f**.......... different,

but it **c**........ change back to how it was **b**............... the change. Three examples:

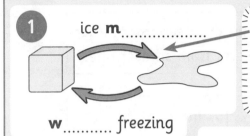

1 ice **m**......................

w............ freezing

All **c**.......................
of **s**.............. are
reversible.

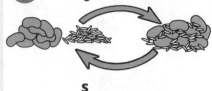

2 mixing beans and rice

s................

3 sugar in water

d..................... sugar

s................

evaporating

sugar

Irreversible Changes

The **f**............
stops the solid.

The **l**..............
passes through.

After an irreversible

change, a completely

d..................... material is

formed, and it **c**...........

change back to how it was

b............... the change.

Three examples:

1 **B**.................
wood to form ash.

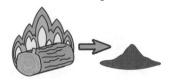

2 **B**............. a cake
mixture into a cake.

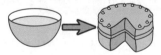

3 Reacting bicarbonate
of soda with **v**............... to
produce carbon **d**................

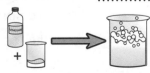

Properties & Changes of Materials Quiz

Now it's time for a quick quiz — how well do you know your materials?

Key Words

1. Draw lines to match the words to their definitions.

Opaque

Solution

Sieving

Insulator

Using a mesh to separate larger solid objects from smaller ones.

A material that you can't see through.

A material that won't let heat or electricity pass through it.

A mixture formed when a solid dissolves in a liquid.

3 marks

Now Try These

2. Write down whether each change below is reversible or irreversible.

a) Baking a cake mixture to make a cake. ....

b) Dissolving sugar in some water
   to make a sugar solution. ....

c) Freezing some water
   to make ice cubes. ....

3 marks

3. Circle the correct word in each of these sentences about magnetic materials.

Some **plastics** / **metals** are magnetic.

Magnetic materials **are** / **aren't** attracted to magnets.

_____
2 marks

4. Write down the best method of separating each of these mixtures.

a) sugar and water ....

b) peas and potatoes ....

c) tea leaves and tea ....

_____
3 marks

5. True or false?
When a solid dissolves in a liquid, you can't see it any more.

....

_____
1 mark

6. Complete each sentence below by picking the most suitable property from the box.

| transparent | hard | insoluble |

a) A window that is see-through needs to be ....

b) A spoon that can stir drinks needs to be ....

c) A hammer that won't break easily needs to be ....

_____
3 marks

Score: [ ]

The Planets, Earth, Sun and Moon

The Solar System

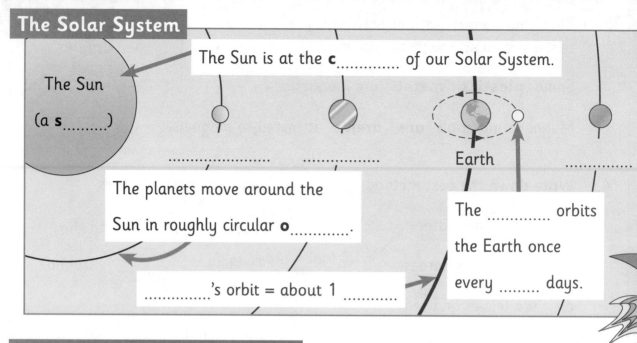

The Sun is at the **c**............ of our Solar System.

The Sun

(a **s**.........)

....

Earth

....

The planets move around the

Sun in roughly circular **o**..............

The .... orbits

the Earth once

every .... days.

...............'s orbit = about 1 ....

Viewing the Moon from Earth

We see the Moon because it **r**................. light from the Sun. The view of the

Moon from Earth **c**................. as it orbits. The view depends on how much

l.......... shines on the side we can see.

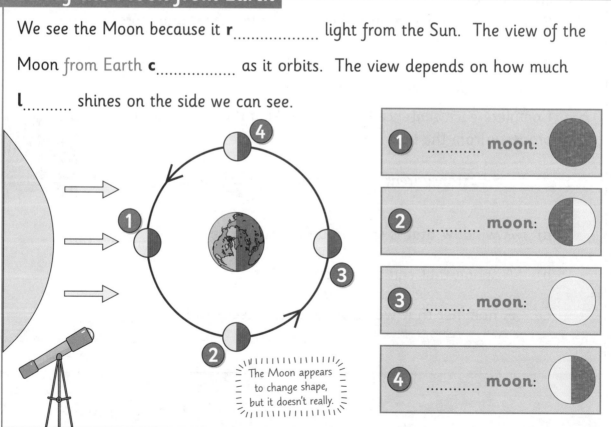

The Moon appears
to change shape,
but it doesn't really.

1 .... **moon**:

2 .... **moon**:

3 .... **moon**:

4 .... **moon**:

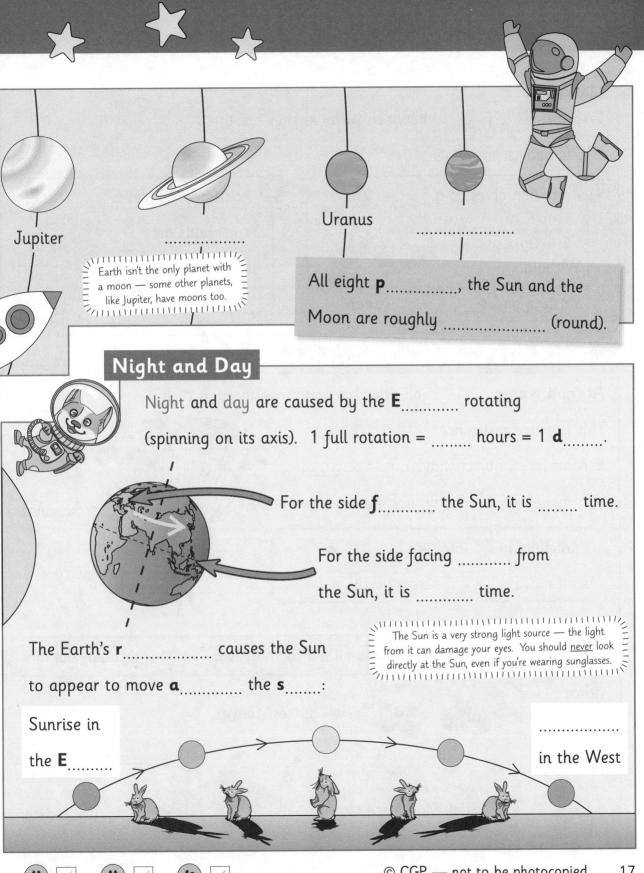

Jupiter

....

Uranus

....

Earth isn't the only planet with a moon — some other planets, like Jupiter, have moons too.

All eight **p**..............., the Sun and the

Moon are roughly .... (round).

Night and Day

Night and day are caused by the **E**............. rotating

(spinning on its axis). 1 full rotation = ... hours = 1 **d**..........

For the side **f**............. the Sun, it is .... time.

For the side facing .... from

the Sun, it is .... time.

The Sun is a very strong light source — the light from it can damage your eyes. You should <u>never</u> look directly at the Sun, even if you're wearing sunglasses.

The Earth's **r**................... causes the Sun

to appear to move **a**........... the **s**.......:

Sunrise in

the **E**..........

....

in the West

Forces and Mechanisms

Friction

Friction is the **f**............ between surfaces that are **t**................. .

It acts against movement.

1   Friction gives us **g**......... .

Trainer soles have lots of grip.

Without .... ,

starting and **s**................. is hard.

2   Friction produces **h**......... .

Your hands get

warm when you

.... them together.

Air Resistance and Water Resistance

Air and **water** .... you down as you move through them.

This is called resistance.

Streamlined objects have a ....

that moves **e**............ through the air or water.

Parachute has a large **s**................. **a**.........

so it moves .... through the air.

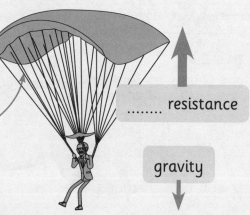

.... resistance

gravity

driving force

Streamlined car moves **q**............... through the air.

air resistance

s........................ shark

driving force

.... resistance

Gravity

Gravity acts between objects and the **E**............

It **p**.......... objects towards the centre of the Earth.

Unsupported objects fall .... the Earth.

Things on the **g**.............. are **P**............ down by gravity too.

> That's why you can't fall off the Earth.

Levers, Pulleys and Gears

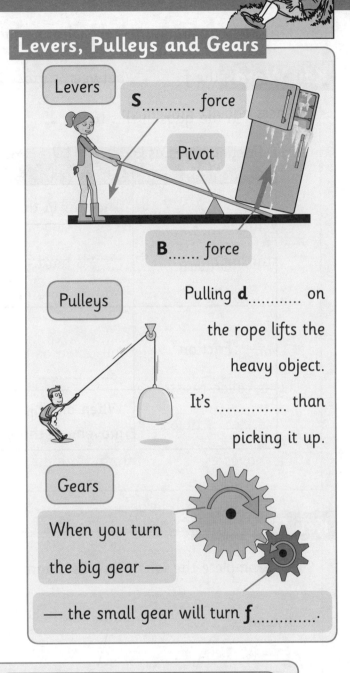

Levers

S............ force

Pivot

B....... force

Pulleys

Pulling **d**............ on the rope lifts the heavy object.

It's .... than picking it up.

Gears

When you turn the big gear —

— the small gear will turn **f**.............

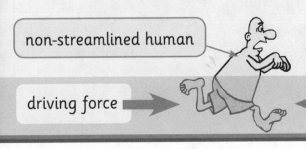

non-streamlined human

driving force

It's **d**.................. to run in water because it **p**.............. against you.

.... resistance

Earth, Space and Forces Quiz

Here are a few questions to test what you've learned on pages 16-19.

Key Words

1. Fill in the gaps in this table.

Word	Definition
....	The star in the centre of our solar system.
Gravity	....
Friction	....
....	When an object has a smooth shape so that movement through air or water is easier.

4 marks

Key Diagrams

2. Complete the labels on this diagram of the Solar System.

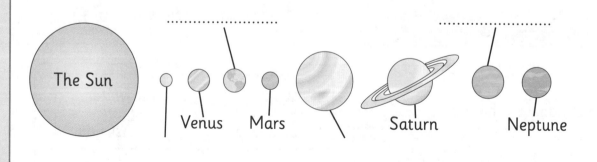

4 marks

3. Use the words in the boxes below to complete the sentences.

    | spherical | light | pulleys | slow |

    a)   Levers, ... and gears can make it easier

    to move things.

    b)   Air and water .... you down as you

    move through them.

    c)   The Moon is roughly ....

    It appears to change shape depending on how much

    .... shines on the side facing Earth.

    _____
    4 marks

4. Complete the answer to each question.
    How long does it take for...

    a)   ... the Moon to orbit the Earth?   28 ....

    b)   ... the Earth to orbit the Sun?   1 ....

    c)   ... the Earth to rotate once?   24 ....

    _____
    3 marks

5. Complete these sentences to describe two effects of friction.

    Friction gives us ...., making it easier for objects to stop

    and start. Friction also produces .... (which is why your

    hands get warm when you rub them together).

    _____
    2 marks

Score: [   ]

Working Scientifically

Planning an Experiment

1 Write down the .... you want to answer.

2 Write a **m**............... for the experiment. This should include:

- what you will measure/observe,
- what **e**..................... you will use,
- how you will make it a .... test.

To make an experiment **f**......., change one **v**.................. at a time and keep everything else the .... (A **v**.................. is anything that could **a**............... your results.)

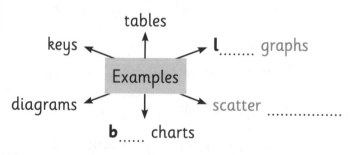

Patterns in Results

Your results may form a **p**....................

E.g.:

Thickness (mm)	Temperature (°C)
4	54
8	58
12	62
16	41

Results that don't fit the .... might suggest that a **m**............... has been made in your experiment.

If possible, **r**..................... your experiment a few times to make sure your results are **r**.....................

Displaying Results

Think about how best to display your ....

tables

keys ← **Examples** → **l**........ graphs

diagrams ← → scatter ....

b...... charts

The best way depends on your **e**.......................

Conclusions

Your experiment should end with a conclusion — a **s**................. that sums up your **f**.................

The sentence is usually written like: 'As one thing changes like this, another thing changes like this.'

3 Make a .... (what you think will happen).

Scatter Graphs

Plot your .... on a grid, then draw **o**........ line that goes as close to .... the points as possible.

Line Graphs

Plot your .... on a grid, then join them up with **s**................. lines.

Growth of a child from 0-2 years

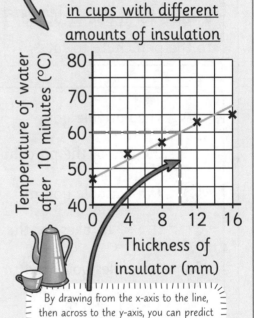

Length of child's body (cm) / Age (months)

Temperature of water in cups with different amounts of insulation

Temperature of water after 10 minutes (°C) / Thickness of insulator (mm)

Line graphs are often used to show how something changes over ....

By drawing from the x-axis to the line, then across to the y-axis, you can predict the temperature for different thicknesses, e.g.: 'The temperature will be 60 °C when the insulator is 10 mm thick.'

Explain whether there were any

P.................... with your experiment:

· Did you make any **m**.................?

· Did all the .... fit with the pattern?

· Could the test have been more fair?

P........................... with the experiment might mean your results are not reliable — if so, you might want to do further **t**................. .

 ☑ ☑ ☑

Investigation – Falling Objects

1 What question do you want to answer?

How does the size of a parachute affect the time it takes for a ball attached to the parachute to fall?

2 How will you do your experiment?

1. Make five square p.......................... out of paper, each one with a d..................... side length. Use a r.......... to measure the side lengths.

A B C D E

Ⓐ Ⓑ The variable you .... is the size of the parachute.

The variable you m................. is the t......... it takes for the ball to fall.

Some variables you need to c................. (keep the same) are:

• the b........ you use,

• where the ball is d................. from,

• the conditions (e.g. the wind).

2. Attach one of the paper parachutes to a b......... Drop the ball from a h........ place (e.g. a balcony or window).

3. Using a ...., get someone standing on the ground to measure the .... between the ball being dropped and it reaching the ground.

4. Repeat steps 2 and 3 for all five p...........................

Results

3 What do you predict will happen?

The larger the parachute, the longer it will take the ball to fall.

Side length of paper parachute (cm)	10	20	30	40	50
Time taken for the ball to fall to the ground (s)	2	4	6	7	9

Plot the results from the table on the scatter graph.

It'd be good practice to repeat the experiment a few times to make sure these results are reliable.

You could plan similar experiments to test further questions, for example:

 How does the shape of the .... affect the .... it takes the ball to fall?

 How does the **w**............. of the ball affect the .... it takes to fall?

Time taken for a ball to fall with different parachutes attached

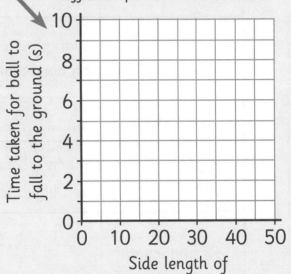

Time taken for ball to fall to the ground (s) — Side length of paper parachute (cm)

You can make predictions based on your results that you could test with further experiments. E.g. you could use the graph to predict how long it would take a ball with no parachute attached to fall.

Conclusion

The results show that the **l**............. the parachute is, the **m**......... time it takes for the .... to fall to the ground.

Mixed Quiz

The moment we've all been waiting for. Let's get down to quizness.

1. Fill in the gaps in the table below.

Word	Definition
....	How easily a material can be scratched or bent.
Conclusion	....
....	Water pushing back against an object moving through it.
Transparent	....
....	When a solid breaks up completely in a liquid to make a solution.
Reproduction	....
....	A change that can be undone — you can get the starting materials back once the change has happened.
Mixture	....

8 marks

2. Use words from the box to complete the definitions below.
You won't need to use all of the words.

> orbit   change   solution
> stigma   asexual   variable   force
> fertilised   sexual   parent

a) .... reproduction: when part of a plant grows into a

new plant. It requires only one ....

b) .... reproduction: when an egg is ....

and then grows into a new plant or animal.

c) ....: a factor in an experiment

that you can control, ... or measure.

6 marks

3. Draw lines to match up each word with its definition.

| Air resistance |

| When a liquid is heated up and changes into a gas. |

| Evaporating |

| Air pushing back against an object moving through it. |

| Filtering |

| What you think will happen in an experiment. |

| Prediction |

| A process you can use to separate a solid from a liquid. |

3 marks

4. The Moon is given different names at different points in its orbit, based on how much of it can be seen from Earth.
Fill in each gap below with the correct name.

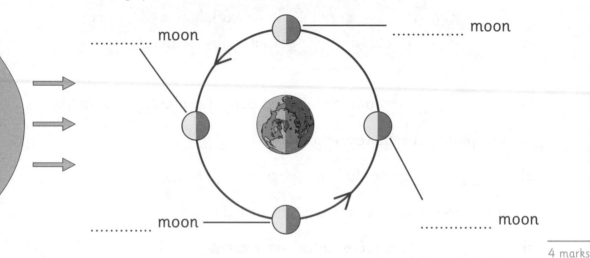

.... moon

.... moon

.... moon

.... moon

4 marks

5. Label these stages in the human life cycle.

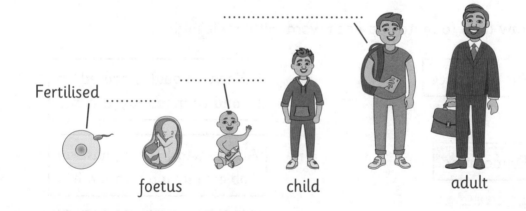

Fertilised ....

....

....

foetus   child   adult

3 marks

6. Circle the correct word to complete the sentence.

Sieving / filtering can be used to separate a mixture of solids.

1 mark

7. Fill in the gaps to complete the life cycle of a butterfly.

Chrysalis

....

Butterfly

2 marks

8. Write down whether each sentence is true or false.

Pushing with a small force on the long side
of a lever will produce a bigger force on
the short side of the lever.   ....

Using a pulley for heavy objects is
easier than picking them up.   ....

Turning a big gear will make a connected
small gear turn more slowly.   ....

3 marks

9. Puberty affects both boys and girls.

a)   Write down one change that happens to boys' bodies, but not
     girls' bodies, during puberty.

     ....

b)   Write down one change that happens to **both** girls' and boys'
     bodies during puberty.

     ....

2 marks

10. Circle the correct word to complete the sentence.

The shape of the Earth is roughly **spherical / cylindrical**.

1 mark

11. What can you do to check that the results of an experiment are reliable?

....

....

12. Write down whether each sentence is describing **sexual** reproduction or **asexual** reproduction.

It involves pollen fertilising an egg. ....

Humans reproduce in this way. ....

Only one parent is needed for reproduction. ....

13. Fill in the gaps to describe the life cycle of a bird.

The life cycle of a bird starts with the mother

laying an .... The chick develops ....

the egg, and later .... from the egg.

The chick then grows into a bird.

14. A parachute has a large surface area, so it moves slowly through the air.

a) What force pushes **up** against the parachute?

....

b) What force pulls the parachute **down** towards the Earth?

....

15. Write down whether each change below is **reversible** or **irreversible**.

   a) Burning wood into ash.

      ....

   b) Mixing beans and rice.

      ....

   c) Ice melting into water.

      ....

3 marks

16. Write down three things that a method for an experiment should include.

   1. ....

   2. ....

   3. ....

3 marks

17. Fill in the gaps to explain night and day on Earth.

Night and day are caused by the Earth ....

For the side facing the Sun, it is .... time.

For the side facing away from the Sun, it is .... time.

3 marks

Score:

Answers

Pages 2-3 — Reproduction

Reproduction

Reproduction: When new **living** things are made, e.g. baby animals or new plants.

Two types of reproduction:

1. **Asexual**
   Only **one** parent needed.
2. **Sexual**
   Two parents needed —
   a male and a **female**.

Animal Reproduction

Animals reproduce by **sexual** reproduction.

Egg from female.
Sperm from male.
Sperm **fertilises** egg.
Fertilised **egg** becomes an embryo.
Embryo grows into a **baby**.

Sexual reproduction happens like this in other **animals** too, not just humans.

Plant Reproduction — Sexual

Stigma: **Female** part of flower.

Pollen: From **male** part of flower.

Pollination — **pollen** transferred to the **stigma** of another plant.

Egg fertilised by the **pollen**.

Fertilised **egg** becomes a **seed**.

Seed germinates into a **seedling**.

Seedling grows into a plant.

Plant Reproduction — Asexual

In asexual reproduction, **new** plants grow from parts of a parent plant (without using **pollen** and **eggs**).

1. Start with the **parent** plant.
2. **Cut** off small parts.
3. Put the small parts in **soil**.
4. The small parts grow into
   new plants.

A plant growing from a bulb is also an example of **asexual** reproduction.

Pages 4-5 — Life Cycles: Animals

Life Cycles

Life cycle — the series of **changes** a living thing goes through during its **life**, including **reproduction**.

The Cat Life Cycle

Cats are **mammals**.
Their life cycle starts with a **fertilised** egg growing **inside** the mother.

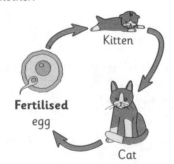

Mammals, like humans, give **birth** to **live** babies.

The Owl Life Cycle

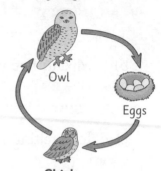

Owls are **birds**.
Their life cycle starts with the **mother** laying fertilised eggs in a nest.

The chick develops **inside** the egg, and later **hatches** from the egg.

The Butterfly Life Cycle

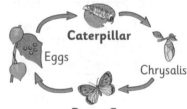

Most **insects**, like butterflies, **lay** fertilised eggs near a **food** source. E.g. many butterflies **lay** eggs onto the leaves and branches of **plants**.

The Frog Life Cycle

Frogs are **amphibians**.
Their life cycle starts with the mother **laying** fertilised eggs in water.

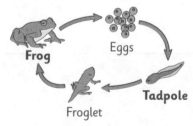

Answers

Pages 6-7 — Life Cycles: Humans

Human Life Cycle

Humans are mammals. The human life **cycle** starts with a fertilised egg **growing** inside the **mother**.

Adults **reproduce** to create **babies**.

fertilised egg → **foetus** → baby → **child** → **adolescent** → adult → **old** age → death

Puberty happens during **adolescence**.

Puberty

Puberty — body **changes** between 10 and 18 **years**.

Different for **girls** and **boys**.

Puberty — Girls

Body **hair** grows
Hips widen
Breasts develop
Ovaries start releasing **eggs** and **periods** start

Puberty — Boys

Facial hair grows
Body hair grows
Testicles start producing **sperm**

Pages 8-9 — Reproduction & Life Cycles Quiz

Key Words

1. Pollination — **When pollen is carried from one flower to the stigma of another**.
   Life cycle — **The stages that a plant or animal goes through during its life**.
   Puberty — When the body changes and develops during adolescence. (3 marks)

Key Diagrams

2.
   egg   egg is **fertilised** by sperm
   sperm   egg becomes an **embryo**, which grows into a baby
   (4 marks)

Now Try These

3. a) **cat** (1 mark)
   b) **owl** (1 mark)
4. Any three from: e.g. **body hair grows**, **breasts develop**, **hips widen**, **ovaries start releasing eggs/periods start** (3 marks)
5. **True**
   False
   True (3 marks)
6. **Pollen** from one flower is transferred to the **stigma** of another flower. This causes an egg to be **fertilised** and become a seed. The seed **germinates** into a seedling, which will become a plant. (4 marks)

Pages 10-11 — Comparing Everyday Materials

Hardness

Hard materials are difficult to scratch or bend.

Materials that aren't hard are **soft**.

Different materials have different **properties**, e.g. hard, soluble, magnetic, etc. The **properties** of a material affect what we use it for.

Transparency

Transparent materials are see-through, e.g. glass.

Opaque materials are not see-through, e.g. thick curtain fabric.

Magnetic Materials

Some metals can be **magnetic** (**attracted** to magnets), while non-metals can't.

But not all metals are **magnetic**, e.g. aluminium, steel.

Solubility

Insoluble materials don't dissolve, e.g. metal spoon and **ceramic** mug.

Soluble materials dissolve, e.g. sugar cubes.

Conductors of Heat

Thermal insulators don't let much heat pass through them. E.g. the **wooden** spoon and the plastic handle.

Thermal conductors let heat pass through them easily. E.g. the **metal** pan.

Thermal **insulators** can keep heat in or out. E.g.
warm clothes
drink flask for hot or **cold** drinks.

Answers

Conductors of Electricity

Electricity can flow through electrical **conductors**.

E.g. **metal** pins and copper **wire**.

Electrical **insulators** can't carry electricity. E.g. the plastic case and insulated flex are **safe** to touch without getting a shock.

Wood, plastic, glass and rubber are all electrical **insulators**. Most metals are good electrical **conductors**.

Never touch bare or frayed wires — electricity can be **conducted** through wires into your body, giving you an electric **shock**.

Pages 12-13 – Separating & Changing Materials

Dissolving

Some solids **dissolve** in liquids to form a **solution**.

For example:
Sugar dissolves in tea and coffee. Gravy granules dissolve in **water**.

When a solid dissolves, you can't **see** it anymore.

Mixtures

A mixture is just things mixed **together**.

Rice in water
A **solution** of salt and water
Peas mixed with potatoes

Separating Mixtures

The separating method depends on the **mixture**:

1. **Sieving** — e.g. to separate peas from potatoes.
   Use a mesh **sieve**.
   The **bigger** bits don't go through.
   The **smaller** bits do.

2. **Filtering** — e.g. to separate tea leaves from tea.
   The **filter** stops the solid.
   The **liquid** passes through.

3. Evaporation — e.g. to **separate** sugar from a sugar solution.
   Heat the solution.
   The liquid **evaporates**.
   The solid is left behind.

Reversible Changes

After a reversible change, the material **looks** and **feels** different, but it **can** change back to how it was **before** the change.
Three examples:

1. ice **melting**
   water freezing

All **changes** of **state** are reversible.

2. mixing beans and rice
   sieving

3. sugar
   dissolving sugar in water
   evaporating
   sugar **solution**

Irreversible Changes

After an irreversible change, a completely **different** material is formed, and it **can't** change back to how it was **before** the change. Three examples:

1. **Burning** wood to form ash.

2. **Baking** a cake mixture into a cake.

3. Reacting bicarbonate of soda with **vinegar** to produce carbon **dioxide**.

Pages 14-15 — Properties & Changes of Materials Quiz

Key Words

1. Opaque — **A material that you can't see through.**
   Solution — **A mixture formed when a solid dissolves in a liquid.**
   Sieving — **Using a mesh to separate larger solid objects from smaller ones.**
   Insulator — **A material that won't let heat or electricity pass through it.**
   (3 marks for all lines drawn correctly, otherwise 2 marks for at least two lines drawn correctly or 1 mark for one line drawn correctly)

Now Try These

2. a) **Irreversible** (1 mark)
   b) **Reversible** (1 mark)
   c) **Reversible** (1 mark)

3. Some **metals** are magnetic. Magnetic materials **are** attracted to magnets. (2 marks)

Answers

4. a) **Evaporating** (1 mark)
    b) **Sieving** (1 mark)
    c) **Filtering** (1 mark)
5. **True** (1 mark)
6. a) A window that is see-through needs to be **transparent**. (1 mark)
    b) A spoon that can stir drinks needs to be **insoluble**. (1 mark)
    c) A hammer that won't break easily needs to be **hard**. (1 mark)

Pages 16-17 —
The Planets, Earth, Sun and Moon

The Solar System

Labels:
The Sun (a **star**) → **Mercury** → **Venus** → Earth → **Mars** → Jupiter → **Saturn** → Uranus → **Neptune**

The Sun is at the **centre** of our Solar System.

The planets move around the Sun in roughly circular **orbits**.

Earth's orbit = about 1 **year**

The **Moon** orbits the Earth once every **28** days.

All eight **planets**, the Sun and the Moon are roughly **spherical** (round).

Viewing the Moon from Earth

We see the Moon because it **reflects** light from the Sun. The view of the Moon from Earth **changes** as it orbits. The view depends on how much **light** shines on the side we can see.

1) **New** moon
2) **Half** moon
3) **Full** moon
4) **Half** moon

Night and Day

Night and day are caused by the **Earth** rotating (spinning on its axis). 1 full rotation = **24** hours = 1 **day**.

For the side **facing** the Sun, it is **day** time.
For the side facing **away** from the Sun, it is **night** time.

The Earth's **rotation** causes the Sun to appear to move **across** the **sky**:
Sunrise in the **East**
Sunset in the West

Pages 18-19 — Forces and Mechanisms

Friction

Friction is the **force** between surfaces that are **touching**. It acts against movement.

1) Friction gives us **grip**.
   Without **grip**, starting and **stopping** is hard.
2) Friction produces **heat**.
   Your hands get warm when you **rub** them together.

Air Resistance and Water Resistance

Air and water **slow** you down as you move through them. This is called resistance.

Streamlined objects have a **shape** that moves **easily** through the air or water.

Parachute has a large **surface area** so it moves **slowly** through the air.
air resistance
gravity

Streamlined car moves **quickly** through the air.

streamlined shark
driving force
water resistance

non-streamlined human
driving force
water resistance

It's **difficult** to run in water because it **pushes** against you.

Gravity

Gravity acts between objects and the **Earth**. It **pulls** objects towards the centre of the Earth.
Unsupported objects fall **towards** the Earth.
Things on the **ground** are **pulled** down by gravity too.

Levers, Pulleys and Gears

Levers
Small force
Pivot
Big force

Pulleys
Pulling **down** on the rope lifts the heavy object. It's **easier** than picking it up.

Gears
When you turn the big gear —
— the small gear will turn **faster**.

Answers

Pages 20-21 — Earth, Space and Forces Quiz

Key Words

1. **Sun** — The star in the centre of our solar system.
   Gravity — **The force that pulls everything towards the centre of the Earth.**
   Friction — **The force between touching surfaces that acts against movement.**
   Streamlined — When an object has a smooth shape so that movement through air or water is easier.
   (4 marks)

Key Diagrams

2.

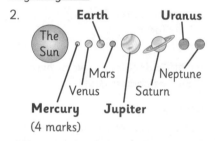

Earth   **Uranus**

The Sun

Mars   Neptune

Venus   Saturn

Mercury   **Jupiter**

(4 marks)

Now Try These

3. a) Levers, **pulleys** and gears can make it easier to move things. (1 mark)
   b) Air and water **slow** you down as you move through them. (1 mark)
   c) The Moon is roughly **spherical**. It appears to change shape depending on how much **light** shines on the side facing Earth. (2 marks)

4. a) 28 **days** (1 mark)
   b) 1 **year** (1 mark)
   c) 24 **hours** (1 mark)

5. Friction gives us **grip**, making it easier for objects to stop and start. Friction also produces **heat** (which is why your hands get warm when you rub them together). (2 marks)

Pages 22-23 — Working Scientifically

Planning an Experiment

1. Write down the **question** you want to answer.
2. Write a **method** for the experiment. This should include:
   • what you will measure/observe,
   • what **equipment** you will use,
   • how you will make it a **fair** test.

To make an experiment **fair**, change one **variable** at a time and keep everything else the **same**.
(A **variable** is anything that could **affect** your results.)

3. Make a **prediction** (what you think will happen).

Patterns in Results

Your results may form a **pattern**.

Results that don't fit the **pattern** might suggest that a **mistake** has been made in your experiment.

If possible, **repeat** your experiment a few times to make sure your results are **reliable**.

Displaying Results

Think about how best to display your **results**.

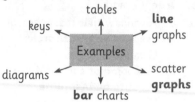

tables

keys   **line** graphs

Examples

diagrams   scatter **graphs**

bar charts

The best way depends on your **experiment**.

Line Graphs

Plot your **results** on a grid, then join them up with **straight** lines.

Line graphs are often used to show how something changes over **time**.

Scatter Graphs

Plot your **results** on a grid, then draw **one** line that goes as close to **all** the points as possible.

Conclusions

Your experiment should end with a conclusion — a **sentence** that sums up your **findings**.

Explain whether there were any **problems** with your experiment:
• Did you make any **mistakes**?
• Did all the **results** fit with the pattern?
• Could the test have been more fair?

Problems with the experiment might mean your results are not reliable — if so, you might want to do further **tests**.

Answers

Pages 24-25 — Investigation — Falling Objects

Planning your Experiment

1. Make five square **parachutes** out of paper, each one with a **different** side length. Use a **ruler** to measure the side lengths.

2. Attach one of the paper parachutes to a **ball**. Drop the ball from a **high** place (e.g. a balcony or window).

3. Using a **stopwatch**, get someone standing on the ground to measure the **time** between the ball being dropped and it reaching the ground.

4. Repeat steps 2 and 3 for all five **parachutes**.

The variable you **change** is the size of the parachute.
The variable you **measure** is the **time** it takes for the ball to fall.
Some variables you need to **control** (keep the same) are:

· the **ball** you use,
· where the ball is **dropped** from,
· the conditions (e.g. the wind).

You could plan similar experiments to test further questions, for example: How does the shape of the **parachute** affect the **time** it takes the ball to fall?
How does the **weight** of the ball affect the **time** it takes to fall?

Results

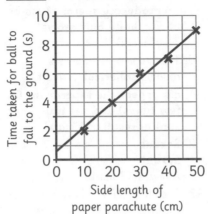

Conclusion

The results show that the **larger** the parachute is, the **more** time it takes for the **ball** to fall to the ground.

Pages 26-31 — Mixed Quiz

Key Words

1. **Hardness** — How easily a material can be scratched or bent.
   Conclusion — **A simple sentence that sums up what you found out in an experiment**.
   Water resistance — Water pushing back against an object moving through it.
   Transparent — **A material that you can see through**.
   Dissolve — When a solid breaks up completely in a liquid to make a solution.
   Reproduction — **Making new living things — animals have babies, plants grow new plants**.
   Reversible change — A change that can be undone — you can get the starting materials back once the change has happened.
   Mixture — **When two or more different materials are mixed together**.
   (8 marks)

2. a) **Asexual** reproduction: when part of a plant grows into a new plant. It only requires one **parent**. (2 marks)

   b) **Sexual** reproduction: when an egg is **fertilised** and then grows into a new plant or animal. (2 marks)

   c) **Variable**: a factor in an experiment that you can control, **change** or measure. (2 marks)

Answers

3. Air resistance — **Air pushing back against an object moving through it**.
    Evaporating — **When a liquid is heated up and changes into a gas**.
    Filtering — **A process you can use to separate a solid from a liquid**.
    Prediction — **What you think will happen in an experiment**.
    (3 marks for all lines drawn correctly, otherwise 2 marks for at least two lines drawn correctly or 1 mark for one line drawn correctly)

Key Diagrams

4.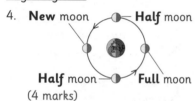
    New moon — **Half** moon
    Half moon — **Full** moon
    (4 marks)

5.
    Fertilised **egg**   **Adolescent**   **Baby**
    foetus   child   adult
    (3 marks)

Now Try These

6. **Sieving** can be used to separate a mixture of solids. (1 mark)

7.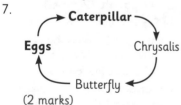
    Eggs → **Caterpillar** → Chrysalis → Butterfly →
    (2 marks)

8. **True**
    True
    False (3 marks)

9. a) E.g. **testicles start producing sperm**. (1 mark)
    b) E.g. **body hair grows**. (1 mark)

10. The shape of the Earth is roughly **spherical**. (1 mark)

11. E.g. **repeat the experiment (a few times) and see if you get similar results**. (1 mark)

12. **Sexual**
    Sexual
    Asexual (3 marks)

13. The life cycle of a bird starts with the mother laying an **egg**. The chick develops **inside** the egg, and later **hatches** from the egg. The chick then grows into a bird. (3 marks)

14. a) **Air resistance** (1 mark)
    b) **Gravity** (1 mark)

15. a) **Irreversible** (1 mark)
    b) **Reversible** (1 mark)
    c) **Reversible** (1 mark)

16. E.g.
    What you will measure or observe.
    What equipment you will use.
    How you will make it a fair test. (3 marks)

17. Night and day are caused by the Earth **rotating**. For the side facing the Sun, it is **day** time. For the side facing away from the Sun, it is **night** time. (3 marks)

55NR21